Usborne

Little Sparkly Princesses Sticker Book

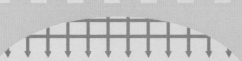

Designed and illustrated
by Lauren Ellis and
Stella Baggott

Words by Kirsteen Robson

Additional design by Winsome d'Abreu

You'll find
all the stickers
at the back of
the book.

The princesses enjoy rides out
in their golden carriage...

...pulled along by their
faithful pony, Flapjack.

A bright, breezy day has dawned at the palace.

The princesses are always up early,
and as busy as bees.

At the fair the princesses love watching the archery contests.

They are looking forward to the ladies' competition,
where they can show off their skills with a bow and arrow.

The treasury is full of jewels that have been in the royal family for hundreds of years.

It's never too early for a mouthful
of coffee and cake. Mmmmm...!

On crisp, icy winter days, the princesses
have fun gliding around on the frozen lake.

The princesses love to walk through the meadows...

...enjoying the fresh air and sunshine.

Merry music fills the air and
the princesses are ready to
dance at the masked ball.

Guided by moonlight and starlight, the princesses like to visit their forest friends.

Pages 2-3

Stick on some shimmering butterflies.

Pages 4-5

Fill the castle with princesses, and the air with birds.

Pages 6-7

Add a splendid banner
and target to the scene.

Page 8

Put glittering crowns
on the model heads.

Page 9

Lay out these treats on the table.

Pages 10-11

Show some sparkling snowflakes.

Pages 12-13

Add some insects glinting in the sunlight.

Pages 14-15

Stick on some dazzling decorations.

Page 16

Fill the sky with glimmering stars.

Pages 2-3

Add more flowers and bees.

Pages 4-5

Stick on flags and flowers.

Pages 6-7

Fill the field with flowers.

Page 8

Add more gems and jewels.

Page 9

Show more delicious delicacies.

Pages 10-11   Arrange the royal skaters on the ice.

Pages 12-13

Cover the meadow with flowers.

Scatter stars everywhere!

Add more princesses and animals.